The Chartered Financial Analyst® Program

EXAM NAVIGATOR
CFA® Level II
Half-Way There Mock Examination

2012

BPP
LEARNING MEDIA

Published January 2012

ISBN 978 1 4453 8309 5

British Library Cataloguing-in-Publication Data
A catalogue record for this book
is available from the British Library

Published by

BPP Learning Media Ltd
BPP House, Aldine Place
London W12 8AA

www.bpp.com/learningmedia

Printed in Great Britain

Your learning materials, published by BPP Learning Media Ltd, are printed on paper sourced from sustainable, managed forests.

Questions 1 through 6 relate to Ethical and Professional Standards

Rosario Santayana Case Scenario

Rosario Santayana joined Calatrava, a firm providing investment services for high net worth clients in Madrid, five years ago. On joining Calatrava, Santayana was assigned to the equities team, and under the mentorship of Viacheslav Sidorov, she became skilled in various equity analysis and stock valuation techniques. Santayana recently obtained the CFA charter, having passed the CFA® Level III examination the year before.

Santayana's older brother, Miguel, is a modern art dealer and gallery owner, and Santayana always attends any new artist exhibition openings. Over the past few years she has befriended several of Calatrava's clients who are avid modern art collectors, meeting them regularly at the exhibition openings hosted by her brother.

Santayana has also befriended several of the up-and-coming young artists that exhibit at her brother's gallery, including Jaime Ortiz, a successful installation artist. Due to the successful sale of several of Jaime's more recent works, Jaime has found himself with substantial monies which he wishes to invest, and asks for Rosario's assistance.

Before agreeing to assist Jaime, Santayana reviews Calatrava's compliance policy regarding independent practice:

Calatrava Wealth Management Compliance Policy

Independent Practice Where an employee of Calatrava wishes to provide investment services on an independent basis, the employee must provide the firm with a written confirmation from their client stating that he or she does not wish to use the services of the Calatrava.

Santayana estimates that managing Jaime's investments will require no more than three to four hours a week, which she plans to fit in on Sunday mornings. Since Santayana doesn't normally work on Sunday, and she feels she has sufficient free time to undertake the work, Santayana judges that the commitment will not interfere with her responsibilities to Calatrava and its clients.

Santayana arranges to meet Jaime and discuss his objectives the following Sunday. She obtains Jaime's written confirmation that he does not wish to use the services of Calatrava, and establishes a preliminary asset allocation for Jaime.

On Monday morning, Santayana provides her supervisor at Calatrava with Jaime's written confirmation, along with a detailed summary of the proposed consulting work, including the nature of the services to be provided, the duration of the work and the compensation arrangements.

One year later, with Jaime's portfolio performing well; Santayana's brother Miguel suggests she set up a business for herself. He tells her "you're supposed to be the one who knows about money in this family, yet you earn a modest salary working at Calatrava. You now have enough experience and contacts to start working for yourself – looking after Jaime's money should convince you of that much".

With the encouragement of her brother and Jaime Ortiz, Santayana decides to take steps to incorporate her own private client wealth management firm and obtain the relevant regulatory approvals. Santayana starts to arrive at work one hour early every day to work on her preparations before the office becomes busy.

Shortly after she has completed her preparations, Santayana provides Calatrava with notice of her resignation. Under the terms of her employment contract, Santayana is required to work a three month notice period before she can cease employment. Viacheslav Sidorov, her long-time mentor at Calatrava, warns her against using the equity evaluation and stock valuation techniques she learned from him. He tells her "I developed your understanding of equity evaluation for the benefit of Calatrava – you can't use these skills to compete with Calatrava when you leave".

Two weeks later, Santayana meets several of Calatrava's clients at an exhibition opening at her brother's gallery. She tells them of her resignation and asks them if they would be interested in the services of her new firm once she has left Calatrava. She obtains several agreements to discuss the matter further once she has worked out her notice period.

After completing her notice period, Santayana launches her new firm.

The first client to commit to Santayana's services instructs her to direct its trades through KIK Brokers. In a preliminary meeting with KIK Brokers, Santayana manages to negotiate the provision of informational services to assist in the management of her investor's funds in return for directing all her transactions through KIK. Whilst KIK charges higher than average fees, she reviews the proposed agreement, and considers that the above average fees are good value given that the informational services provided will enable her to expand her client base more easily. She explains the directed brokerage arrangement carefully to prospective clients, and asks them to sign a waiver stating that they understand that all trades will be directed through KIK Brokers, that KIK Brokers will not necessarily provide the best price and execution, and that Santayana will receive information services to assist in the management of their funds in return for the directed brokerage.

She quickly obtains several clients and invests their money applying the experience and skill in equity analysis and valuation she was tutored in by Sidorov.

One prospective client asks about Santayana's track record. She tells him "I have been managing the affairs of the renowned installation artist, Jaime Ortiz, and he has done extremely well under my management". She proceeds to show the prospective client details of the portfolio she has constructed for Ortiz and the prospective client is impressed with the outstanding returns she has achieved. Convinced by her methods, he agrees to engage Santayana to manage his affairs.

1. Does Santayana *most likely* violate any CFA Institute Standards in accepting the consulting work for Jaime Ortiz?

    A. No, because she provided the appropriate written confirmation from Jaime.

    B. Yes, because the work could be undertaken by Calatrava.

    C. Yes, because she does not provide adequate disclosure to Calatrava.

2. When preparing to establish an investment firm, does Santayana violate any CFA Institute Standards of Professional Conduct?

    A. No.

    B. Yes, because she commenced preparations before resigning.

    C. Yes, because she engages in preparations at the office

3. Did Santayana's actions at the exhibition opening *most likely* violate the CFA Institute Standards of Professional Conduct?

    A. Yes.

    B. No, because she no longer owes a duty of loyalty to Calatrava.

    C. No, because she arranged for discussions to take place after she ceased to be an employee of Calatrava.

4. Which of the following explains why Santayana's relationship with KIK Brokers would *most likely* violate CFA Institute Standards?

    A. Santayana is only allowed to use KIK Brokers for the client that requested her to do so.

    B. Santayana should seek best execution for her clients' accounts if she is to direct brokerage through KIK.

    C. Santayana is prohibited from accepting inducements in return for directed brokerage.

5. Does Santayana *most likely* violate any CFA Institute Standards of Professional Conduct by using the equity analysis and valuation techniques she learned at Calatrava in her new firm?

    A. No.

    B. Yes, because Sidorov expressly prohibited their use.

    C. Yes, because she uses them to compete with Calatrava.

6. Concerning the prospective client who enquires about her track record, which of the following CFA Institute Standards is Santayana *most likely* to have violated?

    A. Suitability.

    B. Preservation of confidentiality.

    C. Communication with client.

Questions 7 through 12 relate to Ethical and Professional Standards

AII Case Scenario

AII is a medium sized investment advisory firm offering investment services and products to retail and institutional clients. The firm operates various equity and fixed income funds, and has recently adopted the CFA Institute Research Objectivity Standards and implemented policies in compliance with the required and recommended policies and procedures.

Brendan Gavin, CFA, works as an investment analyst at AII, covering financial institutions, and has just completed a research note on Medway Banking Corp for the investment committee, as the Equity Income Fund has a substantial holding in Medway. His detailed research indicates that the bank has grown very aggressively but has poor internal risk management procedures and may well be under-capitalized. Gavin is due to present his research to the investment committee the following morning.

Gavin also holds shares in Medway in his personal account, which he had intended to sell in order to finance the deposit on a new house he is buying. That evening, Gavin reviews AII's compliance policies regarding personal dealing. He is concerned that if AII implement his sell recommendation quickly, Medway's stock price will fall and the amount realized will be insufficient to finance the deposit.

AII Compliance Policy Extracts

Personal account trades. All personal account transactions in subject companies and industries, including securities and related derivatives, must be notified to, and approved by the compliance department in advance of any trade.

Priority of trades. The interests of outside clients must be given priority over transactions in securities or other investments of which the employee is the beneficial owner. In addition, transactions in the name of AII must have priority over transactions in securities or other investments of which the employee is the beneficial owner.

Having considered the firm's compliance policies, Gavin decides the best course of action is to sell his holding in Uptown Reinsurance. Gavin recently published a buy recommendation on Uptown, but the stock has languished and thus far failed to reach the target price he published in his latest research note.

The following morning Gavin presents his report to the investment committee. The investment committee decides that whilst Gavin has a reasonable and adequate basis for his recommendation, the report should be sent to Medway to be checked for factual accuracy before any final decision is made. Later that morning, Gavin e-mails the full report to Medway's investor relations department and asks them to verify the factual components of the report.

On the same morning, Gavin notifies compliance of his wish to sell his holding in Uptown Reinsurance. He receives authority from compliance on the same day, and places an order to sell his entire holding in the afternoon. Before he leaves work for the day, Gavin receives confirmation that the sale has been executed, and is relieved that the price achieved will provide him with the entire amount required to finance the deposit on his house purchase.

Fiona Connolly, CFA, is the star portfolio manager at AII. She manages AII's International Fixed Income Fund, and has consistently outperformed the relevant benchmarks. As a renowned stock-picker, Connolly has been invited to speak at an investment conference for investment professionals on financial services stocks.

As a member of the investment committee which received Gavin's report on Medway, Connolly is aware of his concerns regarding the banks level of capitalization, and decides Medway would be a good subject for her presentation. Connolly reviews AII's latest published recommendation as well as Gavin's unpublished report. The latest published research from AII recommended buying into Medway on the strength of the company's strong growth and high return on equity.

At the investment conference Connolly presents her opinions on the need to understand the balance between the positive implications of high return on equity and the negative implications of undercapitalization in the banking sector, using Medway to illustrate. She describes how what appeared to be a good story for Medway is turning into bad news, and concludes that Medway is overpriced given the risk of potential undercapitalization. In summary, she recommends selling Medway.

During a question and answer session following her presentation, Connolly is asked about her remarkable stock-picking abilities. In part, she attributes this to her qualifications. Connolly makes the following three statements:

1.   "The CFA designation represents the highest set of credentials in the investment management industry".

2.   "Having passed all CFA examinations at the first attempt, I belong to an elite that can grasp investment characteristics before the crowd".

3.   "I am able to achieve enhanced portfolio performance as a result of the rigorous and comprehensive study program I undertook in obtaining the CFA charter".

After the conference, a participant requests a copy of All's latest published report on Medway. Connolly tells the participant that the latest research can be purchased through All's web-site for a nominal amount.

7.   Does All's statement on Priority of Trades *most likely* violate the CFA Institute Standards of Professional Conduct?

   A. No.

   B. Yes, because transactions for clients have priority over transactions in securities or other investments of which the employer is the beneficial owner.

   C. Yes, because the interests of clients must be given priority over family accounts and accounts registered in the name of All itself.

8.   Does Gavin's action in sending his research report to Medway's investor relations department *most likely* violate the CFA Institute Research Objectivity Standards?

   A. No, because only confirmation of factual information is being solicited.

   B. Yes, because Gavin's proposed sell recommendation has been communicated.

   C. Yes, because Gavin is prohibited from communicating any contents of the research to the subject company.

9.   Does Gavin's action in selling his holding in Uptown Reinsurance *most likely* violate the CFA Institute Research Objectivity Standards?

   A. No, because he needed to finance the deposit for his house purchase.

   B. No, because he was disadvantaged by the trade.

   C. Yes, because his action was inconsistent with his latest research report on Uptown.

10.   Which of Connolly's statements *most likely* comply with the requirements and recommendations of the CFA Institute Standards of Professional Conduct?

   A. Statement 1.

   B. Statement 2.

   C. Statement 3.

11. Is Connolly's sell recommendation on Medway *most likely* consistent with both the requirements and recommendations of the CFA Institute Research Objectivity Standards?

    A. Yes, because the conference is only accessible to investment professionals.

    B. Yes, because there is a reasonable and adequate basis for the recommendation.

    C. No.

12. Is Connolly's response to the conference participant *most likely* consistent with both the requirements and recommendations of the CFA Institute Research Objectivity Standards?

    A. Yes.

    B. No, because All research should only be made available to All clients.

    C. No, because research referenced at a conference should be made available to all participants at no cost.

Questions 13 through 18 relate to Quantitative Methods

Peggy Parsons CFA wants to forecast sales of BoneMax, a prescription drug for treating osteoporosis. Osteoporosis is a degenerative disease that primarily affects women over the age of 60.

Parsons has developed the sales regression model shown in Exhibit 1 and supporting data found in Exhibits 2 through 5 to assist in her sales forecast of BoneMax.

EXHIBIT 1
BONEMAX SALES REGRESSION MODEL

$$SALES = 8.530 + 6.078 (POP) + 5.330 (INC) + 7.380 (ADV)$$

t-statistics: (2.48) (2.23) (2.10) (2.75)

Unadjusted R^2 = 0.370

Sample standard deviation of sales = $12m

Number of observation = 20 annual observations

Durbin-Watson coefficient: 1.66

Notes

SALES = sales of BoneMax (U.S.$ millions)

POP = population (millions) of U.S. women over age 60

INC = average income (U.S.$ thousands) of U.S. women over age 60

ADV = advertising dollars spend on BoneMax (U.S.$ millions)

EXHIBIT 2
VARIABLE ESTIMATES FOR 2010

POP	34.7
INC	27.4
ADV	8.2

EXHIBIT 3
CRITICAL VALUES FOR STUDENT'S T-DISTRIBUTION

Degrees of Freedom	Area in Upper Tail		
	10%	5%	2.5%
16	1.3368	1.7459	2.1199
17	1.3334	1.7396	2.1098
18	1.3304	1.7341	2.1009
19	1.3277	1.7291	2.0930
20	1.3253	1.7247	2.0860

EXHIBIT 4
CRITICAL VALUES FOR THE F-DISTRIBUTION (RIGHT-HAND TAIL AREA = 0.05)

Degrees of Freedom for the Denominator	Degrees of Freedom for the Numerator					
	1	2	3	4	5	6
15	4.54	3.68	3.29	3.06	2.90	2.79
16	4.49	3.63	3.24	3.01	2.85	2.74
17	4.45	3.59	3.20	2.96	2.81	2.70
18	4.41	3.55	3.16	2.93	2.77	2.66
19	4.38	3.52	3.13	2.90	2.74	2.63
20	4.35	3.49	3.10	2.87	2.71	2.60
21	4.32	3.47	3.07	2.84	2.68	2.57
22	4.30	3.44	3.05	2.82	2.66	2.55
23	4.28	3.42	3.03	2.80	2.64	2.53
24	4.26	3.40	3.01	2.78	2.62	2.51
25	4.24	3.39	2.99	2.76	2.60	2.49
26	4.22	3.37	2.97	2.74	2.58	2.47
27	4.20	3.35	2.95	2.72	2.56	2.45
28	4.19	3.34	2.94	2.71	2.55	2.44
29	4.18	3.33	2.93	2.70	2.54	2.43
30	4.17	3.32	2.92	2.69	2.53	2.42
31	4.16	3.30	2.91	2.68	2.52	2.41
32	4.15	3.29	2.90	2.67	2.51	2.40
33	4.14	3.28	2.89	2.66	2.50	2.39
34	4.13	3.28	2.88	2.65	2.49	2.38
35	4.12	3.27	2.87	2.64	2.49	2.37
36	4.11	3.26	2.87	2.63	2.48	2.36
37	4.11	3.25	2.86	2.63	2.47	2.36
38	4.10	3.24	2.85	2.62	2.46	2.35
39	4.09	3.24	2.85	2.61	2.46	2.34
40	4.08	3.23	2.84	2.61	2.45	2.34
41	4.08	3.23	2.83	2.60	2.44	2.33
42	4.07	3.22	2.83	2.59	2.44	2.32
43	4.07	3.21	2.82	2.59	2.43	2.32
44	4.06	3.21	2.82	2.58	2.43	2.31
45	4.06	3.20	2.81	2.58	2.42	2.31

EXHIBIT 5
CRITICAL VALUES FOR THE DURBIN-WATSON STATISTIC ($\alpha = 0.05$)

n	k = 1		k = 2		k = 3	
	d_L	d_U	d_L	d_U	d_L	d_U
27	1.32	1.47	1.24	1.56	1.16	1.65
28	1.33	1.48	1.26	1.56	1.18	1.65
29	1.34	1.48	1.27	1.56	1.20	1.65
30	1.35	1.49	1.28	1.57	1.21	1.65
31	1.36	1.50	1.30	1.57	1.23	1.65
32	1.37	1.50	1.31	1.57	1.24	1.65
33	1.38	1.51	1.32	1.58	1.26	1.65
34	1.39	1.51	1.33	1.58	1.27	1.65
35	1.40	1.52	1.34	1.58	1.28	1.65
36	1.41	1.52	1.35	1.59	1.29	1.65
37	1.42	1.53	1.36	1.59	1.31	1.66
38	1.43	1.54	1.37	1.59	1.32	1.66
39	1.43	1.54	1.38	1.60	1.33	1.66
40	1.44	1.54	1.39	1.60	1.34	1.66
41	1.44	1.55	1.40	1.60	1.35	1.67
42	1.45	1.55	1.41	1.61	1.36	1.67
43	1.46	1.56	1.42	1.61	1.37	1.67
44	1.47	1.56	1.43	1.62	1.38	1.67
45	1.48	1.57	1.43	1.62	1.38	1.67

13. Which of the following is *closest to* the forecast sales for BoneMax for 2010?

A. $342m

B. $417m

C. $426m

14. Which of the following is *closest to* the F-statistic for a test concerning whether all the independent variables taken simultaneously have a significant relationship with the dependent variable and what is the appropriate conclusion for the test at a significance level of 5%?

A. The F-statistic is 3.33 and the null hypothesis should not be rejected.

B. The F-statistic is 3.13 and the null hypothesis should be rejected.

C. The F-statistic is 3.13 and the null hypothesis should not be rejected.

15. Given the information above, which of the statements below is *most accurate*?

 I   The regression coefficient of the population of U.S. women over the age of 60 (POP) is statistically significantly different from zero at the 5% level of significance

 II The regression coefficient of the average income of U.S. women over the age of 60 (INC) is statistically significantly different from zero at the 5% level of significance

	STATEMENT I CORRECT?	STATEMENT II CORRECT?
A.	Yes	Yes
B.	Yes	No
C.	No	Yes

16. Which of the following is closest to a 95% confidence interval for the regression coefficient estimate of population of U.S. women over the age of 60 (POP)?

 A. 0.30 to 11.86

 B. 1.31 to 10.84

 C. 3.35 to 8.81

17. Which of the following is *closest to* the standard error of the estimate (in millions)?

 A. 10

 B. 11

 C. 12

18. Which of the following is *most likely* to be the appropriate conclusion with respect to a test regarding serial correlation?

 A. Conclude that there is positive serial correlation.

 B. Conclude that there is negative serial correlation.

 C. Conclude that there is no serial correlation.

Questions 19 through 24 relate to Economics

Marge Farrell CFA is a currency manager for Ganz International. Ganz currently has a large net position in U.S. dollars, which must be fully invested. In anticipation of the company's need for Avalon marks (AM) in six months, Farrell is investigating the investment alternatives. She finds that the annual rate on 180-day U.S. Treasury bills is 6.0%, while the corresponding rate on similar instruments in the country of Avalon is 4.5%. She believes that various factors may slow the adjustment of spot and forward exchange rates and thus allow deviations from interest rate parity to exist temporarily, but only in the short run. The prevailing exchange rates are shown in Exhibit 6.

EXHIBIT 6
FOREIGN EXCHANGE RATE QUOTATIONS

Exchange Rates	U.S.$ per AM	AM per U.S.$
Spot rate	0.4900	2.0408
90-day forward rate	0.4930	2.0284
180-day forward rate	0.4961	2.0157

If Farrell determines that an investment in AM is advantageous now, she will also attempt to enhance returns by identifying arbitrage opportunities in the cross rates between AM and other currencies, which are shown in Exhibit 7.

EXHIBIT 7
CURRENCY CROSS RATES

Country	U.S.$	Swiss Franc	Aus$	Yen	AM
Avalon	2.0408	1.2460	1.5512	0.01960	–
Japan	104.74	63.944	79.614	–	51.021
Australia	1.3156	0.8032	–	0.01256	0.64466
Switzerland	1.638	–	1.2450	0.01564	0.8026
United States	–	0.61050	0.76011	0.00955	0.4900

Mike Land, a colleague of Farrell, has developed a model-based forecast, using fundamental analysis and the concept of purchasing power parity (PPP). Land believes that the threat of rising inflation will prompt the Avalon central bank to tighten the money supply in Avalon within the next six months. He forecasts that for the next year the U.S. inflation rate will average 2%, while the Avalon rate of inflation is expected to average 5%.

19. Based on the 180-day forward rate, the annualized forward premium or discount on the AM is *closest to* a:

A. 2.5% discount.

B. 1.2% premium.

C. 2.5% premium.

20. With respect to interest rate parity and the possible flow of short-term funds, which of the following statements *best describes* the U.S. dollar-mark relationship?

   A. The dollar and the mark are not at interest rate parity, and there is no advantage to short-term movement of funds.

   B. The U.S. interest rate advantage is more than offset by the forward premium on the mark, and short-term funds will tend to move to Avalon.

   C. The forward premium on the mark is more than offset by the U.S. interest rate advantage, and the short-term funds will tend to move to the U.S.

21. If Farrell wants to acquire Avalon marks and take advantage of triangular arbitrage opportunities, she is *most likely* to buy:

   A. marks directly.

   B. Swiss francs and sell them for marks.

   C. Japanese yen and sell them for marks.

22. Based on Land's forecast, the expected U.S.\$/AM spot rate in six months is *closest to*:

   A. 0.4760

   B. 0.4829

   C. 0.4972

23. Empirical evidence indicates that relative purchasing power parity appears to hold:

   A. in the short run but not over longer periods of time.

   B. over longer periods of time but not in the short run.

   C. in the short run and over longer periods of time.

24. If Farrell believes that Land's forecast is accurate, she is *most likely* to invest in:

   A. U.S. T-bills now, and expect to acquire marks in the spot market at lower rates 180 days from now.

   B. U.S. T-bills now, and buy marks for 180-day forward delivery.

   C. marks now, and expect to acquire dollars in the spot market at lower rates 180 days from now.

Questions 25 through 30 relate to Financial Reporting and Analysis

Kai Hubert Case Scenario

Kai Schlepper, CFA, is an equity research analyst for a global investment bank covering defense industry stocks. Hubert is preparing a note on defense sector, examining the remuneration structure in the industry. In particular, Schlepper wishes to examine the widespread use of stock-based compensation and the provision of defined benefit pension plans. Schlepper's note will focus on two key players in the sector - Aerospace Technologies Corp.(ATC) and Fortress Inc. (FI). Both entities report under US GAAP and both have adopted both SFAS 123 (stock-based compensation) and SFAS 158 (pension accounting) in their latest annual reports (31 December 2010).

Schlepper extracts the following information from the note on Stock-based compensation from the annual reports of the two entities:

EXHIBIT 8
STOCK OPTION VALUATION DISCLOSURE EXTRACTS – ATC

	2010
Basis of option valuation	Black-Scholes
Share Price at 1 January 2010	$25.22
Exercise price as % of closing stock price on grant date	100%
Time to expiry	9 years
Dividend yield assumed	1.9%
Volatility assumed	41.0%
Risk-free rate assumed	3.8%
Fair value of options at grant date, 1 January 2010	$6.79
Number of options granted at 1 January 2010 (million)	5.20
Vesting period	4 years

EXHIBIT 9
STOCK OPTION VALUATION DISCLOSURE EXTRACTS - FI

	2010
Basis of option valuation	Black-Scholes
Share Price at 1 January 2010	$38.17
Exercise price as % of closing stock price on grant date	120%
Time to expiry	8 years
Dividend yield assumed	2.1%
Volatility assumed	29.0%
Risk-free rate assumed	4.1%
Fair value of options at grant date, 1 January 2010	$7.11
Number of options granted at 1 January 2010 (million)	8.30
Vesting period	3 years

Based on his analysis of the disclosures, Schlepper concludes that overall, the assumptions used by ATC are more conservative, and would lead to a higher stock-based compensation expense (all other things equal).

Schlepper also examines the disclosures on pensions for both companies, and extracts the funded status of the plans (Exhibit 10) for both entities:

EXHIBIT 10
PENSION PLAN FUNDED STATUS AS OF 31 DECEMBER 2010 ($ MILLIONS)

Funded Status of the Plan	ATC	FI
Projected Benefit Obligation at 1 January 2010	442.1	765.9
Service cost	31.1	39.9
Interest cost	24.3	38.3
Employee contributions	2.3	0.0
Benefits paid	(18.8)	(14.9)
Actuarial (gains)/losses	13.4	(6.5)
Projected Benefit Obligation at 13 December 2010	494.4	822.7
Fair value of plan assets at 1 January 2010	412.9	806.6
Actual return on plan assets	(7.9)	(17.7)
Employer contributions	35.4	47.4
Employee contributions	2.3	0.0
Benefits paid	(18.8)	(14.9)
Fair value of plan assets at 31 December 2010	423.9	821.4
Unrecognized actuarial losses	36.5	99.1
Unrecognized prior service cost	4.3	21.6

The expected return on plan assets anticipated by ATC was $28.9 million, and $52.4 million for FI.

Schlepper also wishes to contrast the assumptions being used by each entity, and extracts the following actuarial assumptions from the pension disclosure notes for both entities:

EXHIBIT 11
SELECTED PENSION PLAN ACTUARIAL ASSUMPTIONS

Pension plan assumptions and other information	ATC	FI
Expected return on assets	7.8%	6.4%
Discount rate for obligations	5.9%	4.8%
Expected rate of compensation increases	2.2%	2.1%
Actual return on assets	(2.9%)	(2.2%)

Based on his analysis of the disclosures, Schlepper concludes that overall, the assumptions used by FI are more conservative, and would lead to a higher net periodic pension expense and Projected Benefit Obligation (all other things equal).

Schlepper identifies that ATC is amortizing unrecognized actuarial losses and past service costs through the income statement over 10 years, and that the amounts charged in 2010 were $4.1 million and $0.5 million respectively.

25. When comparing the underlying assumptions used by ATC and FI to determine the fair value of options, which assumption used by FI is *least* consistent with Schlepper's overall conclusion that ATC's assumptions are more conservative?

   A. The dividend yield.

   B. The share price volatility.

   C. The risk-free rate.

26. The stock-based compensation expense charged by ATC during 2010 is *closest* to:

   A. 3.923 million.

   B. 8.827 million.

   C. 35.308 million.

27. Under SFAS No.158, the amount recognized on the balance sheet of FI in respect of its pension plan at 31 December 2010 is *closest* to:

   A. 119.4 million net asset.

   B. 1.3 million net liability.

   C. 122.0 million net liability.

28. The economic pension expense for 2010 for ATC is *closest* to:

   A. 58.7

   B. 63.3

   C. 76.7

29. When comparing the underlying assumptions used by ATC and FI to determine the PBO, which assumption used by ATC is *least* consistent with Schlepper's overall conclusion that FI's assumptions are more conservative?

   A. Discount rate.

   B. Expected return on plan assets.

   C. Expected rate of compensation increases.

30. The net periodic pension expense for ATC in 2010 is *closest* to:

   A. $31.1 million.

   B. $35.7 million.

   C. $40.3 million.

Questions 31 through 36 relate to Financial Reporting and Analysis

Hortense Boulanger Case Scenario

Hortense Boulanger works as a credit analyst supporting the fixed income team at GMR asset managers. Boulanger has been asked to analyze the creditworthiness of Calico Technologies, a U.S. based company manufacturing specialist microchips for use in a wide range of domestic and industrial appliances. The fixed income team has asked Boulanger to prepare a net asset valuation of Calico Technologies, and to analyze the quality of earnings and free cash flow generation of the business.

Calico Technologies reports under US GAAP, and summary financial statements for Calico Technologies are presented below in Exhibits 12 to 14:

EXHIBIT 12
CONDENSED INCOME STATEMENT OF CALICO TECHNOLOGIES FOR THE YEARS ENDED 31 SEPTEMBER
(US$ MILLION)

	2010	2009
Net sales	48,883	39,556
Cost of goods sold (COGS)	(35,754)	(28,654)
Selling, general & administrative expenses (SG&A)	(9,649)	(8,531)
Interest expense (net of interest income)	(532)	(519)
Profit before tax	2,948	1,852
Income taxes @33%	(973)	(611)
Net income	1,975	1,241

EXHIBIT 13
CONDENSED BALANCE SHEET OF CALICO TECHNOLOGIES FOR THE YEARS ENDED 31 SEPTEMBER
(US$ MILLION)

Assets	2010	2009
Cash and cash equivalents	295	2,308
Trade accounts receivable	1,987	1,786
Inventories	9,343	8,408
Property, plant, and equipment (net of accumulated depreciation)	12,076	9,975
Goodwill	255	255
Total assets	23,956	22,732

Liabilities and Shareholders' Equity	2010	2009
Trade accounts payable	4,033	3,410
Advances from customers	500	400
Long term debt	7,300	8,800
Deferred tax liabilities	348	322
Shareholders' equity	11,775	9,800
Total liabilities and shareholders' equity	23,956	22,732

Upon detailed examination, Boulanger establishes that Calico Technologies has shortened the estimated useful life of its property, plant and equipment (PP and E). She also ascertains that Calico uses LIFO to determine the cost of inventory, and that the LIFO reserve amounts to $500 million.

BPP
LEARNING MEDIA

She also notes that Calico Technologies has entered a significant number of operating leases. She has estimated that, should the operating leases be capitalized, they would amount to $2,600 million.

Boulanger has also examined the financial statements from the prior three year, and she has noticed that the deferred tax liability has increased over each of the years she has examined.

In addition, Boulanger notes that Calico Technologies has sold receivables with limited recourse during 2010.

EXHIBIT 14

CONDENSED CASH FLOW STATEMENT OF CALICO TECHNOLOGIES FOR THE YEARS ENDED 31 SEPTEMBER

(US$ MILLION)

	2010	2009
Net income	1,975	1,241
Depreciation and amortization	872	775
(Increase) decrease in working capital	(413)	(321)
Increase (decrease) in deferred tax liability	26	22
Cash flow from operating activities (CFO)	2,460	1,717
Additions to property, plant, and equipment	(3,038)	(1,372)
Disposition of property and equipment	65	50
Cash flow from investing activities (CFI)	(2,973)	(1,322)
Redemption of long term debt	(1,500)	0
Cash flow from financing activities (CFF)	(1,500)	0
Net increase (decrease) in cash and cash equivalents	(2,013)	395

Boulanger decides it will also be helpful to calculate the accruals ratio for Calico Technologies. For simplicity, Boulanger calculates the ratios using unadjusted balance sheet numbers.

31. Which of the following would *least likely* indicate a lower quality of earnings for Calico Technologies to Boulanger?

A. The shortening of the estimated useful life of PP and E.

B. The significant use of operating leases.

C. The sale of receivables with partial recourse.

32. The impact of Boulanger's adjustments for operating leases, LIFO and deferred tax liabilities to the unadjusted number of Calico Technologies is *most likely* to:

A. increase total liabilities by $2,252 million.

B. increase total liabilities by $2,600 million.

C. increase total liabilities by $3,100 million.

33. Which of the following items is *least likely* to cause an increase in the adjusted total assets of Calico Technologies?

A. Boulanger adjusting for operating leases.

B. Boulanger adjusting for LIFO inventory costing.

C. Boulanger adjusting for goodwill.

34. When Boulanger adjusts the published financial statements of Calico Technologies, which of the following items is *most likely* to cause an increase in the total debt of Calico Technologies?

A. Advances from customers.

B. Deferred tax liabilities.

C. Sale of receivables with limited recourse.

35. Boulanger's calculation of the balance sheet accruals ratio for Calico Technologies is *closest* to:

A. 13.25%.

B. 14.07%.

C. 14.19%.

36. Calico Technologies free cash flow to the firm for 2010 is *closest* to:

A. –$157 million.

B. –$183 million.

C. –$222 million.

Questions 37 through 42 relate to Corporate Finance

Weston Cambridge, CFA, is a senior analyst for Massa Partners. Cambridge is analyzing the proposed acquisition of Country Winery by Hartford Wines. Hartford Wines is a California-based bulk-wine producer that makes wines under 12 brand names. Hartford controls 20,000 acres of California vineyards, processes approximately 220,000 tons of grapes each year, and produces roughly 16 million cases of wine, most of which is sold in bulk to other wine companies. Country has a substantial vineyard business, farms grapes for other wineries, and has an outsourcing business where it does custom winemaking. Country owns approximately 8,000 acres in southern California.

On Tuesday, May 12, Hartford made a $60 per share cash offer for all of the outstanding shares of Country. In a press release, Hartford provided the following justifications for the proposed acquisition:

- **Justification 1**: The combined company's larger balance sheet should improve access to debt and capital markets, enabling Hartford to access funds at a lower borrowing cost.

- **Justification 2**: The combined company will have a significantly larger market capitalization, which will improve the liquidity of its shares and increase trading turnover on major stock exchanges, resulting in a broadening of the investor base and increasing shareholder value.

- **Justification 3**: The combined operation will be fully integrated, with significant cost reductions resulting from reduced production and freight costs, increased leverage from marketing expenditures, and improved vineyard management. Economies of scale will give the combined company increased flexibility, efficiency, and quality control over the grape supply.

- **Justification 4**: The combined company will significantly diversify its revenue and earnings base, and reduce its exposure to downturns in the business cycle.

On Monday, May 11, shares of Hartford closed at $38 and Country shares closed at $52. There are 1,000,000 shares of Hartford Wines outstanding and 500,000 outstanding shares of Country Winery.

Cambridge analyzes the bottom line impact of the proposed cost savings and revenue enhancements over the next ten years, as shown in Exhibit 15. He assumes that any incremental cash flows resulting from the acquisition will be zero after ten years.

EXHIBIT 15

Year	Incremental Cash Flow	Present Value at Estimated Cost of Capital
1	$2,000,000	$1,804,509
2	$1,600,000	$1,302,501
3	$1,600,000	$1,175,187
4	$1,600,000	$1,060,317
5	$1,000,000	$597,922
6	$800,000	$431,582
7	$800,000	$389,397
8	$200,000	$87,834
9	$200,000	$79,248
10	$200,000	$71,502
Total	$10,000,000	$7,000,000

Cambridge makes the following estimates based on his analysis:

Gain (to Hartford) from acquisition	$36 million
Cost (to Hartford) of acquisition	$30 million
NPV (to Hartford) from acquisition	$6 million

Cambridge is certain that Country will turn down the original cash offer, and he anticipates an all-stock offer in which Hartford offers 1.75 shares of Hartford for every 1 share of Country. Cambridge expects the stock offer to be accepted by Country's board because it will be earnings per share accretive for Hartford shareholders in the following fiscal year by immediately increasing earnings per share.

Cambridge also reviews some empirical research on the distribution of benefits resulting from mergers and acquisitions, which suggests that sellers earn significantly higher percentage returns on average than buyers. He identifies two primary reasons for this empirical result:

■ **Reason 1**: Competition among potential bidders for the value created as a result of the merger drives up the final price to the point where sellers capture most of the gain.

■ **Reason 2**: Buyers, on average, have much larger market capitalization than sellers.

37. Assuming the calculations in Exhibit 15 are correct, based on the cash price offer, Cambridge has:

A. correctly estimated the NPV of the acquisition to Hartford.

B. overestimated the NPV (to Hartford) of the acquisition by $3 million.

C. underestimated the NPV (to Hartford) of the acquisition by $5 million.

38. *For this question only,* suppose the news that Country was willing to negotiate a takeover leaked to the market prior to the original cash offer on May 11. The market responded by bidding up Country's share price to the point where Country's shareholders captured the entire gain from the merger. Assume that the analysis of incremental cash flows in Exhibit 15 is correct. The new market price and the NPV (to Hartford) of the acquisition are *closest* to:

	NEW MARKET PRICE PER SHARE	NPV OF ACQUISITION
A.	$60	$0
B.	$66	$0
C.	$66	$3 million

39. The cost and the NPV (to Hartford) of the acquisition, based on the 1.75-for-1 stock offer (in millions of dollars), are *closest* to:

	COST OF ACQUISITION	NPV OF ACQUISITION
A.	$7.1	–$0.1
B.	$7.1	$2.7
C.	$4.3	–$0.1

40. Cambridge determines that Justification 4 is not an appropriate justification for the acquisition. Cambridge is:

A. incorrect to question Justification 4, because revenue and earnings diversification leads to greater economies of scale, significant cost savings, and increased shareholder value.

B. correct to question Justification 4, because revenue and earnings diversification will decrease the post-acquisition beta of the combined operations and increase shareholder value.

C. correct to question Justification 4, because risk diversification is not likely to create value for Hartford's shareholders.

41. Cambridge determines that Justification 1 is an appropriate justification for the acquisition because it will significantly increase shareholder value. Cambridge is:

    A. correct to accept Justification 1, because borrowing costs typically decrease after an acquisition.

    B. correct to accept Justification 1, because increased economies of scale in new debt issuance will decrease flotation costs after the acquisition.

    C. incorrect to accept Justification 1, because the lower borrowing costs that result will benefit bondholders but not shareholders.

42. In Cambridge's analysis of the distribution of merger benefits, are Reason 1 and Reason 2 consistent with the result that seller returns in mergers are larger than buyer returns?

	REASON 1	REASON 2
A.	Yes	Yes
B.	Yes	No
C.	No	Yes

Questions 43 through 48 relate to Fixed Income Investments

Donald Sector Case Scenario

Donald Sector, CFA, works as a fixed income analysts at Chartersquare Investments, a fixed income specialist asset manager. Sector has recently been transferred to the asset and mortgage-backed securities division. On his induction day into the division, Lazlo Bakos, head of the division, informs him of the following:

Statement 1: The spread for Mortgage Backed Securities should be calculated using a binomial model of interest rates.

Statement 2: The spread for high quality home equity loan Asset Backed Securities should be calculated using Monte Carlo simulation of interest rates.

Aretha Duncan manages one of Chartersquare's funds, and is concerned that interest rates are on the rise. Her fund is heavily invested in MBS pass-through securities. She asks for Sector's recommendations to reduce the risk posed to her portfolio by rising interest rates. Sector provides the following recommendations:

Statement 3: "Sell the pass-through securities and invest into sequential pay collateralized mortgage obligation (CMO) tranches.

Statement 4: Invest in an interest only (IO) stripped MBS because its value will increase as interest rates rise above the contract rate.

Statement 5: Invest in credit card receivable Asset Backed Securities which are still within the initial lock-out period as they have no prepayment risk."

Duncan asks Sector to estimate the expected prepayment in the next month for a pass-through security she currently holds. Duncan provides Sector with the following information:

EXHIBIT 16
NFORMATION REGARDING PASS-THROUGH SECURITY HELD BY DUNCAN

Principal balance outstanding	$815.2 million
Scheduled monthly principal payment	$21.7 million
Conditional prepayment rate	5.0%

Duncan also asks Sector to provide estimates of the spread for a sequential pay collateralized mortgage obligation (CMO) tranche she is considering. An extract of his results is presented below:

EXHIBIT 17
SPREAD ESTIMATES FOR SEQUENTIAL PAY COLLATERALIZED MORTGAGE OBLIGATION TRANCHE

Zero volatility spread	3.15%
Option adjusted spread (binomial model)	4.14%
Option adjusted spread (Monte Carlo model)	3.98%

Following detailed discussions with Chartersquare's economic forecasting department, Sector is also concerned that interest rates are on the rise. He believes that this environment will favor equities over bonds, and is considering purchasing a convertible bond for his personal account. Exhibit 17 provides details of a convertible security issued by MAW inc. being considered by Duncan.

EXHIBIT 18
MAW INC. CONVERTIBLE SECURITY INFORMATION

Current market price (per $100 par)	$104.82
Annual coupon rate	7.0%
Time to maturity	13 years
Conversion ratio	27 shares per $1,000 par value
Current stock price of MAW Inc.	$29.56
MAW Inc. dividend per share	$0.65
Expected MAW inc. stock price volatility	22.8%

43. Which of Bakos' statements regarding the models used to calculate the spreads for MBS and Home equity loan ABS is/are *most likely* correct?

    A. Statement 1 only.

    B. Statement 2 only.

    C. Statements 1 and 2.

44. What risk do Sector's recommendations in Statements 3, 4 and 5 *most likely* mitigate in Duncan's portfolio?

    A. Contraction risk.

    B. Extension risk.

    C. Maturation risk.

45. Which of Sector's statements to Duncan regarding IO strips and credit card ABS is/are *most likely* correct?

    A. Statement 4 only.

    B. Statement 5 only.

    C. Statement 4 and 5.

46. Sector's estimate of the expected prepayment relating to the pass-through security, based on the information in Exhibit 16, is *closest* to:

    A. $3.306 million.

    B. $3.385 million.

    C. $3.477 million.

47. Which of the spread measures provided by Sector in Exhibit 17 is *most* appropriate for analyzing the sequential pay collateralized mortgage obligation tranche being considered by Duncan?

    A. 3.15%

    B. 4.14%

    C. 3.98%

48. Sector's estimate of the market conversion premium ratio for the MAW Inc. convertible security shown in Exhibit 18 will be *closest* to:

    A. 9.5%

    B. 24.7%

    C. 31.3%

Questions 49 through 54 relate to Fixed Income Investments

Franco De Cesaris Case Scenario

Franco De Cesaris, CFA, is a fixed income analyst with Pluto Investments Managers. At a morning meeting, his manager, Yuliya Karpov, CFA, informs De Cesaris that she is considering starting a high-yield bond fund. Karpov asks De Cesaris how the emphasis of credit analysis for high-yield issuers differs from that of investment grade issuers. De Cesaris makes the following three statements:

Statement 1: A more detailed analysis of covenants is particularly important for high-yield issuers.

Statement 2: Consideration of the corporate structure of high-yield issuers merits little attention compared with investment-grade issuers.

Statement 3: Analysis of the debt structure for high-yield issuers is much more important than in analyzing the debt structure for investment-grade issuers.

Karpov then instructs De Cesaris to undertake a review of Westman Communications, a European telecoms firm which has been expanding by acquisition in recent years. Westman Communications earlier acquisitions were financed with stock, but more recent acquisitions have seen an increased use of debt financing. The Pluto investment grade fund has a holding of Westman's 8.55% Notes due 2020 and Karpov is concerned that Westman's increased leverage and deteriorating operating performance could prompt a downgrade from BBB to non-investment grade.

Karpov provides De Cesaris with the following summary extracts from Westman Communications' latest financial statements:

EXHIBIT 19
WESTMAN COMMUNICATIONS BALANCE SHEET INFORMATION (€ THOUSANDS)

Assets	2010
Cash and cash equivalents	1,181
Trade accounts receivable (net of allowances)	7,948
Inventories	37,372
Property, plant, and equipment (net of accumulated depreciation)	48,304
Goodwill	1,020
Total assets	95,825
Liabilities and Shareholders' Equity	
Trade accounts payable	18,132
Long term debt	29,200
Deferred tax liabilities	1,392
Shareholders' equity	47,101
Total liabilities and shareholders' equity	95,825

EXHIBIT 20
WESTMAN COMMUNICATIONS CASH FLOW INFORMATION (€ THOUSANDS)

	2010
Net income	7,901
Depreciation and amortization	3,488
(Increase) decrease in working capital	(1,652)
Increase (decrease) in deferred tax liability	104
Cash flow from operating activities (CFO)	9,841
Additions to property, plant, and equipment	(12,152)
Disposition of property and equipment	260
Cash flow from investing activities (CFI)	(11,892)
Redemption of long term debt	(6,000)
Cash flow from financing activities (CFF)	(6,000)
Net increase (decrease) in cash and cash equivalents	(8,051)

Karpov also provides De Cesaris with the bond prospectus for the 8.55% Notes due 2020, including the following extract:

EXHIBIT 21
WESTMAN COMMUNICATIONS BOND PROSPECTUS EXTRACT

Interest Coverage (extract)

Westman Communications undertakes not to raise additional debt finance unless interest coverage (defined as earnings before interest and tax divided by gross interest payable including capitalized interest), retrospectively adjusted for the additional debt over the two years prior to its issuance, is in excess of 3.5x at each interim and year-end reporting period.

De Cesaris calculates financial ratios for Westman Communications from the latest published financial statements in order to compare them to the median values for ratings in the telecom sector. His results are presented below:

EXHIBIT 22
SELECTED WESTMAN COMMUNICATIONS RATIOS AND MEDIAN RATIO VALUES BY RATING

	Median for BBB rating	Median for BB rating	Westman 2010
Return on capital	12.38%	9.98%	12.27%
Operating margin	18.47%	14.83%	19.12%
EBITDA interest coverage	6.11x	4.96x	6.03x
EBIT interest coverage	4.67x	3.21x	4.61x

49. Which of De Cesaris' statements regarding credit analysis applied to high yield bonds is *most likely* false?

   A. Statement 1.

   B. Statement 2.

   C. Statement 3.

50. Karpov's concern regarding Westman Communications is *best* described as:
    A. downgrade risk.
    B. credit spread risk.
    C. default risk.

51. Westman's quick or acid test ratio (in € thousands) for 2010 is *closest* to:
    A. 0.44
    B. 0.50
    C. 2.56

52. Westman's Discretionary Cash Flow (in € thousands) for 2010 is *closest* to:
    A. -2,311
    B. 9,841
    C. 11,493

53. The covenant described in Exhibit 21 is *best* described as a:
    A. maintenance test.
    B. debt incurrence test.
    C. cash flow test.

54. Given the information provided in Exhibit 22, the *most likely* outcome is that Windmiller's bonds:
    A. will be placed on a positive outlook.
    B. will retain their current rating.
    C. will be downgraded.

Questions 55 through 60 relate to Derivative Investments

Peter Anderson Case Scenario

Peter Anderson is the corporate treasurer at Diamond Industries, an Irish specialist plastics firm headquartered in Dublin. Anderson has been charged with arranging financing for a new UK subsidiary, which will act as a manufacturing base for Diamond's UK operations.

Anderson has been advised by the board that the UK subsidiary will require £40 million in debt financing. The board anticipates that the financing will be required in six months time. He is conscious that the UK subsidiary will not generate any sterling-denominated revenues, and that the debt will need to be services through the parent's euro net revenues.

After some initial enquiries with investment banks, Anderson decides that a bond issue is inappropriate for Diamond Industries given the amount of financing required. Aware of the board's innate conservativism, Anderson decides that fixed interest rate financing will be preferable.

The following week Anderson submits his written proposal to the board for consideration. Extracts from Anderson's report are provided in Exhibit 23 below:

EXHIBIT 23
EXTRACTS OF A REPORT TO THE BOARD CONCERNING FINANCING FOR THE NEW SUBSIDIARY

It is proposed that the new subsidiary is financed with a term loan denominated in euro, which can then be exchanged into sterling.

After enquiries with our bank, the term loan can be raised at an approximate cost of LIBOR plus 200 basis points. Should the board wish, the floating rate borrowings can be converted into fixed rate borrowings with the use of an interest rate swap.

Shortly after Anderson has submitted his proposal to the board, he is asked to attend a special meeting of the board to further discuss his proposals.

At the special board meeting, members of the board are divided with regard to two key issues – the expected direction of interest rates and the expected direction of exchange rate movements between sterling and the euro. The board also expresses concern about dealing in derivatives with an investment bank given recent financial market turmoil. In response, Anderson provides the following information:

Statement 1: "A plain vanilla interest rate swap can fix our borrowing costs. Instead of paying LIBOR plus 200 basis points we can pay a fixed rate of interest plus 200 basis points.

Statement 2: We face no potential credit risk if we enter a pay fixed swap and interest rates rise. However, given uncertainty about the path of interest rates, we can monitor the potential credit risk which is likely to increase over the life of the swap.

Statement 3: As a first alternative to a swap, we could use a FRA or forward rate agreement. This would allow us to be selective about which interest cash flows we fix.

Statement 4: As a second alternative to the swap, we could purchase a payer swaption. Whilst this would cost money, it would give us the flexibility to avoid the swap if interest rates fall.

Statement 5: We could enter a forward contract to buy sterling in six months time at €1.2230 and eliminate currency risk. This can be converted to a synthetic call option with an exercise price of €1.2200 over the sterling if you later decide you want to exploit any strengthening of the euro.

Statement 6: A call option to buy sterling will require an initial premium to be paid. The premium is liable to increase if the euro/sterling exchange rate becomes more volatile, but will become cheaper if we are willing to fix a higher buying price for sterling in the option or if sterling strengthens relative to the euro."

Following the meeting, Anderson is asked to ascertain what the fixed interest rate for a plain vanilla swap is likely to be based on a €50 million two year annual interest term loan taken out today based on LIBOR, reset every six months.

As an alternative, the board also asks Anderson to estimate the fixed rate that could be guaranteed with a FRA for the first six month's interest liability on the same term loan if it the loan were taken out in six months time.

The board also asks Anderson to value a swaption with an annualized exercise rate of 4% expiring in six months at expiration, assuming the resultant swap is matched to the same two year term loan for €50 million taken out in six months time.

Anderson extracts the following data presented in Exhibit 24 to help in his calculations. Anderson assumes all six month periods are of 180 days and each year is of 360 days in his calculations.

EXHIBIT 24
EURO LIBOR RATES

EuroLIBOR rates (annualized)	Rate Today	Discount factor	Rate in 180 days	Discount factor
180-day	3.50%	0.9829	3.90%	0.9811
360-day	3.85%	0.9629	4.10%	0.9606
540-day	3.60%	0.9483	3.80%	0.9456
720-day	4.20%	0.9210	4.35%	0.9184

55. Given the information in Statement 1 and Exhibit 24, and using Anderson's calculation assumptions for the number of days, the annualized fixed rate on the plain vanilla interest rate swap as requested by the board would be *closest* to:

A. 3.83%

B. 3.94%

C. 4.14%

56. Statement 2 can be *best* characterized as:

A. incorrect with respect to potential credit risk if interest rates rise only.

B. incorrect with respect to potential credit risk over the life of the swap only.

C. incorrect with respect to both potential credit risk if interest rates rise and over the life of the swap.

57. Given the information in Statement 3 and Exhibit 24, and using Anderson's calculation assumptions for the number of days, the annualized fixed rate for the FRA as requested by the board would be *closest* to:

A. 3.76%

B. 4.12%

C. 4.32%

58. Given the information in Statement 4 and Exhibit 24, and using Anderson's calculation assumptions for the number of days, the value of the swaption at expiry would be *closest* to:

A. €274,300

B. €365,900

C. €487,200

59   Given the information in Statement 5, which positions would be required to convert the forward contract into a synthetic call option as described by Anderson?

A. Long put option and short zero coupon bond.

B. Long put option and long zero coupon bond.

C. Short put option and long zero coupon bond.

60.   The information in Statement 6 is *incorrect* with respect to:

A. the volatility of the euro/sterling exchange rate.

B. the higher buying price for euro.

C. sterling strengthening relative to the euro.

Ethical and Professional Standards

1. **C** Santayana is obligated to comply with CFA Institute Standards. The Standard relating to Loyalty to Employer requires that Santayana disclose details of the consulting work and receive written consent from Calatrava before rendering service.

   See LOS 2a

2. **C** Santayana has violated her duty of loyalty to Calatrava. According to the Standard relating to Duty to Employer, a departing employee is generally free to make arrangements or preparations to go into a competitive business before terminating the relationship with her employer provided that such preparations do not breach the employee's duty of loyalty. Specifically, prior to leaving an employer, an employee must not work on the new business during working hours or at the office of the existing employer.

   See LOS 2a

3. **A** The clients belong to Calatrava and Santayana is not permitted to solicit their business until after she leaves the firm. Whilst the discussions were arranged for a time after cessation of employment, the solicitation occurs whilst she remains an employee Standard IV (A) – Duties to Employers, Loyalty.

   See LOS 2a

4. **B** According to Standard III (A) Loyalty, Prudence, and Care, members must act for the benefit of their clients and place their clients' interests before their own. Santayana may only trade through KIK if the accounts receive best execution. Santayana puts her own interests ahead of that of her clients when directing brokerage in exchange for services she believes she will allow her to gain new clients.

   See LOS 2a

5. **A** Santayana is permitted to use the methods she learned from Sidorov. Skills and experience that an employee obtains while employed are not confidential or privileged information.

   See LOS 2a

6. **B** The Standards prohibit Santayana from revealing confidential information about clients.

   See LOS 2a

7. **A** Priority should go to clients and employers over accounts in which All personnel are beneficial owners.

   See LOS 2a

8. **B** Gavin is prohibited from sharing any element of a research report with the subject company which might communicate his proposed recommendation.

   See LOS 2b

9. **C** Gavin is prohibited from trading in a manner that is contrary to, or inconsistent with, the employees' or the firms most recently published recommendation, unless he can demonstrate he would suffer extreme financial hardship.

   See LOS 4b

10. **A**   Connolly's statement about the status of the CFA designation is acceptable.

See LOS 2a

11. **C**   The CFA Institute Research Objectivity Standards recommends that firms should prohibit covered employees from communicating a rating or recommendation that is different from the current published rating or recommendation.

See LOS 4b

12. **A**   The CFA Institute Research Objectivity Standards recommend that firms provide full research reports on the subject companies discussed to members of the audience at a reasonable price. At a minimum, the covered employee should disclose whether a written research report is available to members of the audience who are not clients of the firm, the approximate cost, and how a listener might acquire the report. Firms should make copies of the full research report available for purchase or review; for example via the firm's website.

See LOS 4b

Quantitative Methods

13. **C**   Sales = 8.530 + 6.078(34.7) + 5.330(27.4) + 7.38(8.2) = $426m

     See LOS 12c

14. **C**   The null **hypothesis** is that the b coefficients are all simultaneously equal to zero

     The F-statistic is calculated as $\dfrac{0.37 \div 3}{0.63 \div 16} = 3.13$

     The F-statistic has been based on the level of explained variation (0.37) and the level of unexplained variation (1 − 0.37 = 0.63). This will give the same ratio as the regression sum of the squares divided by the sum of the squared errors because

$$R^2 = 0.37 = \frac{\text{Regression sum of the squares}}{\text{Total variation}} \text{ and}$$

$$1 - R^2 = 0.63 = \frac{\text{Sum of the squared errors}}{\text{Total variation}}$$

     Degrees of freedom for numerator = 3

     Degrees of freedom for denominator = 20 − 4 = 16

     Critical value of the F-statistic = 3.24

     Therefore, do not reject the null hypothesis

     See LOS 12e

15. **B**   The number of degrees of freedom is given by sample size less 4, since there are three independent variables and the intercept. The degrees of freedom are therefore 20 − 4 = 16

     The test is two-tailed, since we are testing whether the coefficient is different from zero. The confidence level is 95%, giving a rejection area of 2.5% at either end of Student's t-distribution

     The critical value of the t-statistic is 2.1199

     A regression coefficient is statistically significant from zero if the actual t-tatistic exceeds its critical value. This is the case for both POP and ADV

     For INC the t-statistic is 2.10. Since the t-statistic is less than the critical value of 2.1199, it is not possible to reject the null hypothesis. We cannot state that there is a significant relationship

     See LOS 12b

16. **A**   The standard error for population can be calculated from the following equation

$$\text{t-statistic} = \frac{b - 0}{\text{Standard error}}$$

$$2.23 = \frac{6.078}{\text{Standard error}}$$

Standard error = 2.726

At the 95% level with a two-tailed situation, the relevant t-statistic to use is the same as for (c) above

β = b +/– 2.1199 × Standard error

β = 6.078 +/– 2.1199 × 2.726 = 6.078 +/– 5.78

That is, from 0.30 to 11.86

See LOS 12c

17. **A**   Sample standard deviation = 12 million

$$12 = \sqrt{\frac{\text{Sum of squared deviations}}{n - 1}} = \sqrt{\frac{\text{SSD}}{19}}$$

Sum of squared deviations = 2,736

Sum of squared errors = 0.63 × 2,736 = 1,723.68 (0.63 is the level of unexplained variation = $1 - R^2$)

$$\text{Standard error of the estimate} = \sqrt{\frac{\text{Sum of squared errors}}{n - 4}}$$

$$= \sqrt{\frac{1,723.68}{16}}$$

$$= 10.38$$

See LOS 11f

18. **C**   The critical values of the DW statistic with sample size = 27 and with three independent variables are 1.16 and 1.65. From the pattern of the critical values of the DW statistic in Exhibit 5, we can assume that the critical values for a sample size of 20 will be lower than 1.16 and 1.65 respectively. A DW statistic of 1.66 for a sample of 20 means that it will be above the higher critical value, meaning that we can conclude there is no serial correlation

See LOS 12i

Economics

19. **C** You are asked for the forward premium or discount on the AM, so you should use quotations for the AM in terms of U.S.$. The spot rate is U.S.$0.4900 per AM while the 180-day forward rate is U.S.$0.4961 per AM. The AM is therefore at a premium in the forward market

The annualized forward premium $= \dfrac{0.4961 - 0.4900}{0.4900} \times \dfrac{360}{180} = 0.0249$ or 2.49%

See LOS 17g

20. **B** The U.S. interest rate advantage is 1.5% (i.e. 6.0% – 4.5%), while the forward premium on the AM is 2.5%. Since the AM is quoted at too high a forward premium than that suggested by interest rate parity, an arbitrageur would sell marks in the forward market, and at the same time borrow dollars to buy marks in the spot market. Short-term funds will therefore move to Avalon

See LOS 17h

21. **C** Buying marks directly would cost U.S.$0.4900 per AM

Buying Swiss francs and then selling them for marks

U.S.$1 buys CHF1.638

CHF1.638 buys $1.638 \times 1.2460 = 2.0409$ AM

Therefore, the cost would be $\dfrac{1}{2.0409} =$ U.S.$0.48998 per AM

Buying Japanese yen and then selling them for marks

U.S.$1 buys ¥104.74

¥104.74 buys $104.74 \times 0.01960 = 2.0529$ AM

Therefore, the cost would be $\dfrac{1}{2.0529} =$ U.S.$0.48712 per AM

Buying Australian dollars and then selling them for marks

U.S.$1 buys AUD$1.3156

AUD$1.3156 buys $1.3156 \times 1.5512 = 2.0408$ AM

Therefore the cost would be $\dfrac{1}{2.0408} =$ U.S.$0.49000 per AM

The least costly alternative is to buy Japanese yen and then sell them for marks

See LOS 17d

22. **B** Using relative PPP, the expected spot rate in six months (in terms of U.S.$ per AM)

$= S_0 \times \dfrac{(1+i_F)^t}{(1+i_D)^t} = 0.4900 \times \dfrac{1.02^{0.5}}{1.05^{0.5}} = 0.4829$

See LOS 18h

23.   **B**   In the short run, there are other factors that affect the real exchange rate, e.g. monetary policy, balance of payments, etc.

        See LOS 18g

24.   **A**   Farrell will want to buy marks as cheaply as possible. The quoted 180-day forward rate is $0.4961 per AM. If Land's forecast proves accurate, then the spot rate prevailing in six months' time will be $0.4829 per AM (as calculated in Question 22). Farrell should invest in U.S. T-bills now for six months, then expect to acquire marks in the spot market at lower rates 180 days from now. Note, however, that this rate is not guaranteed as Land's forecast may not be realized

        See LOS 17e

Financial Reporting and Analysis

25. **C** The stock-based compensation expense is based on the fair value of the options as calculated on the option grant date. This has been calculated using the Black-Scholes pricing model. The higher the fair value of the options, the greater the compensation expense, and the more conservative the assumptions.

The fair value is calculated using the stock price, the exercise price, the time to expiry at the grant date and assumptions regarding the future stock price volatility, dividend yield and risk-free rate. Higher volatility, higher risk-free rates and lower dividend yields lead to higher values for the options. Since FI uses a higher risk-free rate than ATC, it is using a more conservative assumption than ATC

See LOS 23j and 56c

26. **B** Stock options are measured at their fair value on the grant date. The fair value is then expensed over the vesting period (4 years)

Total fair value at grant date = $6.79 × 5.2m = $35.308m
Annual expense = $35.308/4 years = $8.827m

See LOS 23j

27. **B** Under SFAS No. 158 the pension liability recognized is the ending pension obligation minus the ending pension assets without any adjustments for unrecognized amounts. 821.4 – 822.7 = 1.3 net liability.

See LOS 23e

28. **C** The economic pension expense would include service cost plus interest cost less actual return on assets plus actuarial losses: 31.1 + 24.3 – 7.9+ 13.4 = 76.7. Alternatively, it is the change in the pension obligation less the change in plan assets adjusted for cash contributions and benefit payments. [Change in benefit obligation – employee contributions + benefits paid *(non-expense item)*] – [Change in plan assets – (contributions – benefits paid)] (494.4 - 442.1 – 2.3 + 18.8) – (423.9 - 412.9 – (35.4+2.3 – 18.8)) = 76.7

See LOS 23h

29. **C** FI has assumed a lower discount rate than ATC. A lower discount rate will increase the present value of the pension liability (PBO) and the service cost. Expected return on assets affects the pension expense, but not the obligation. FI has assumed a lower expected rate of compensation increase than ATC. The lower expected rate of compensation increase would reduce the PBO, and is therefore less conservative than ATC

See LOS 23d

30. **A**

Service cost	31.1
Interest cost	24.3
Expected return on plan assets	(28.9)
Amortization of actuarial losses	4.1
Past service costs	0.5
Net periodic benefit cost	31.1

See LOS 23c

31. **A** Quality of earnings refers to the degree of conservatism in reported earnings. Shortening the estimated useful life of PP and E will lead to higher depreciation charges and is therefore an indication of high earnings quality. Both sale of receivables with partial recourse and the use of operating leases are off-balance sheet financing techniques, which lower the quality of earnings

See LOS 26d

32. **A** Calico's operating leases need to be added to both liabilities and assets. The deferred tax liability has increased every year, suggesting that it is unlikely to reverse; it should therefore be removed from liabilities and added into equity. The LIFO reserve should be added back to inventories, increasing its carrying amount and equity, but having no impact on liabilities

See LOS 27d

33. **C** Calico's operating leases need to be added to both liabilities and assets. The LIFO reserve should be added back to inventories, increasing its carrying amount and equity. Goodwill should be removed from assets and equity

See LOS 27d

34. **C** Advances from customers are a legitimate liability and should not be part of an adjustment of the firm's debt. Deferred tax liabilities which are not expected to reverse should be removed from liabilities. Sale of receivables (with recourse) can be thought of as collateralized borrowing and needs to be part of the adjustment to the debt level

See LOS 27d

35. **C** $$\text{Accrual Ratio (BS)} = \frac{\text{Aggregate Accruals from Balance Sheet}}{\text{Average Net Operating Assets}}$$

Net Operating Assets = Total assets – cash and equivalents) – (Total liabilities – debt)

Aggregate accruals = $\text{NOA}_t - \text{NOA}_{t-1}$

	2010	2009
Total assets	23,956	22,732
Cash and cash equivalents	295	2,308
Operating assets	23,661	20,424
Total liabilities	12,181	12,932
Long term debt	7,300	8,800
Operating liabilities	4,881	4,132
Net Operating Assets	18,780	16,292
Average Net Operating Assets	17,536	
Aggregate Accrual	2,488	
Balance sheet accrual ratio	14.19%	

See LOS 26c

36.   **A**   Free cash flow (FCFF) is defined as the cash flow available to the company's suppliers of capital after all operating expenses (including taxes) have been paid and necessary investments in working capital and fixed capital been undertaken. It can be calculated in two different ways: [1] from the Income Statement, as Net Income plus net non-cash charges (NCC) plus interest expense (net of taxes) less investment in fixed capital less investment in working capital; or, [2] from the Cash Flow Statement as Cash flow from Operations plus interest expense (net of taxes) less investment in fixed capital

Computing FCFF from net income		
Net income	1,975	
plus interest expense, after tax	356	532*(1–.33)
Depreciation and amortization	872	
Net additions to property, plant, and equipment	(2,973)	
(Increase) decrease in working capital	(413)	from CFS
Increase (decrease) in deferred tax liability	26	
FCFF	(157)	
Alternatively,		
Computing FCFF from EBIT		
EBIT	3,480	
Less taxes on EBIT at 33%	(1,148)	
NOPAT	2,332	
Depreciation and amortization	872	
Additions to property, plant, and equipment	(2,973)	
(Increase) decrease in working capital	(413)	
Increase (decrease) in deferred tax liability	26	
FCFF	(156)	
Alternatively,		
Computing FCFF from Cash Flow Statement		
Cash flow from operating activities (CFO)	2,460	
plus interest expense, after tax	356	532* (1–.33)
Additions to property, plant, and equipment	(2,973)	
FCFF	(157)	

See LOS 40d

Corporate Finance

37. **B** The NPV (to Hartford) of the acquisition, based on the cash offer price, is $3 million, so Cambridge has overestimated the NPV by $6 million – $3 million = $3 million

Gain = PV of cost savings and revenue enhancement = $7 million

Cash offer = $60 × 500,000 shares = $30 million

Value of Country before merger = $52 × 500,000 shares = $26 million

Cost = $30 – $26 = $4 million

NPV = gain – cost = $7 – $4 = $3 million

See LOS 32l and 32m

38. **B** If the acquisition price per share is bid up so that Country's shareholders capture the entire gain, the NPV (to Hartford) of the acquisition must equal zero. Hartford must pay $26 million (Country's value before the news leaked) plus the entire $7 million gain, so the new market price per share is $33 million / 500,000 shares = $66 per share

See LOS 32l and 32m

39. **A** If each share of Country is traded for 1.75 shares of Hartford, 500,000 × 1.75 = 875,000 new shares are created. Hartford's value prior to the merger was $38 × 1,000,000 = $38 million. The total value of the combined firm is $38 million + $26 million + $7 million = $71 million

New price = $\frac{\$71 \text{ million}}{1,875,000}$ = $37.87

Gain = $7 million

Stock offer = $37.87 × 875,000 shares = $33.1 million

Cost = $33.1 – $26 = $7.1 million

NPV = gain – cost = $7 – $7.1 = –$0.1 million

See LOS 32l and 32m

40. **C** Hartford is using Justification to argue that the merger will benefit shareholders because it will diversify revenues and earnings. If such diversification reduces the company's exposure to downturns in the business cycle, systematic risk will be reduced and beta will decrease. However, risk reduction through diversification is not likely to create value for Hartford's shareholders. Shareholders can much more cheaply and easily diversify on their own by purchasing shares of both firms for their investment portfolios. Hence Cambridge is correct to determine that Justification is not an appropriate justification for the acquisition

See LOS 32b

41. **C** There are economies of scale in debt issues related to lower flotation costs, investment banking and legal fees, and direct issue costs. However, these cost savings are relatively small. The reason the combined firm can lower borrowing costs after a merger is because it is issuing less risky debt. The bondholders now have stronger protection as the assets of the two previously separate firms back the debt. That makes the bondholders happy but does not increase shareholder wealth, because the shareholders now have to, in effect, guarantee each other's debt. In contrast, as separate entities, a default on one firm's debt could not be paid off with the assets from the other firm

See LOS 32b

42.   **A**   Both reasons are consistent with the result that seller returns are larger than buyer returns. Sellers capture most of the gain if buyers get into a bidding war and drive the cash price higher. In addition, because the buyers are usually larger in terms of market capitalization than the sellers, on average, sellers will earn larger percentage returns on their original investment

See LOS 32m

Fixed Income Investments

43. **B**   Since a MBS prepayment risk is interest rate path-dependent, a Monte Carlo simulation should be used to model the spread, not a binomial tree of interest rates. High quality home equity loans have a prepayment option that is often exercised when interest rates drop and borrowers refinance. Furthermore these cash flows are interest rate path-dependent, and therefore a Monte Carlo simulation of interest rates is appropriate

       See LOS 53i

44. **B**   Sector's recommendations reduce the extension risk posed to Duncan's portfolio – namely the risk that as interest rates rise, the prepayment rate slows

       See LOS 51f

45. **B**   Sector is incorrect with regard to IO value. If mortgage rates rise above the contract rate, the expected cash-flow improves, but the cash flow is discounted at a higher rate. The net effect may be either a rise or a fall in IO value. Sector is correct with regard to prepayment risk for credit card receivables during the lock-out period

       See LOS 51j and 52e

46. **B** $SMM = 1 - (1 - CPR)^{1/12}$
          $SMM = 1 - (1 - 5\%)^{1/12}$
          $SMM = 0.4265\%$

       The estimated prepayment $= 0.4265\% \times (\$815.2 - \$21.7) = \$3.385$ million

       See LOS 51c

47. **C**   Since a MBS prepayment risk is interest rate path-dependent, a Monte Carlo simulation should be used to model the spread, not a binomial tree of interest rates

       See LOS 53i

48. **C**   Market conversion price $= (\$104.82 \times \$1000/\$100)/27 = \$38.82$
          Market conversion premium per share $= \$38.82 - \$29.56 = \$9.26$
          Market conversion premium ratio $= \$9.26/\$29.56 = 31.3\%$

       See LOS 50j

49. **B**   Analyzing the corporate structure for high-yield issuers is key as the analyst will need to understand how the cash flows generated by the operating subsidiaries can be passed up to the holding company

       See LOS 48f

50. **A**   "…the risk attributable to a lowering of the credit rating (i.e., a downgrading) is referred to as downgrade risk"

       See LOS 48a

51. **B**   The quick or acid-test ratio is calculated as current assets excluding inventory divided by current liabilities $= (1,181 + 7,948)/18,132 = 0.50$

       See LOS 48c

52.　**A**　Discretionary cash flow is calculated as Operating cash flow or cash flow from operating activities net of capital expenditure and cash dividends = 9,841 – 12,152= -2,311

See LOS 48c

53.　**B**　In a debt incurrence test, the interest or fixed charge coverage as adjusted for the new debt must be at a minimum level for the required period prior to financing

See LOS 48c

54.　**B**　The ratios are much closer to if not above the median values for the bonds' current BBB rating

See LOS 48d

Derivative Investments

55. **C** The fixed rate on a swap is calculated as (where C=semi-annual coupon):

1= 0.9829C+0.9629C+0.9483C+0.9210C+0.9210

1 = 3.8151C+0.9210

3.8151C = 1-0.9210

C= (1-0.9210)/ 3.8151

C= 2.0707%

Annualized fixed rate = 2.0707% x 360/180 = 4.1414%

See LOS 57c

56. **C** If interest rates rise, the swap will become a net asset to Diamond industries, creating credit risk. The potential credit risk of an interest rate swap is greatest at the middle of its life; it does not increase throughout the life of the swap

See LOS 57j

57. **B** FRA rate (180 day rate) = [(1+360 day LIBOR)/(1+(180 day LIBOR × 180/360)] − 1

FRA rate (180 day rate) = [1.0385/(1+(0.0350 × 180/360)] − 1

FRA rate (180 day rate) = 2.06%

FRA rate (annualized) = 2.06% × 360/180 = 4.12%

See LOS 54c

58. **A** The fair fixed rate for the two year swap, given the rates in 180 days is calculated as (where C=semi-annual coupon):

1= 0.9811C + 0.9606C + 0.9456C + 0.9184C + 0.9184
1 = 3.8057C + 0.9184
3.8057C = 1 − 0.9184
C= (1-0.9184)/ 3.8057
C= 2.1442%

Annualized fixed rate = 2.1442% × 360/180 = 4.2884%

Given the exercise price of 4%, the value at expiry is given by:

(4.000% − 4.2884%) (180/360) × €50 million × (0.9811 + 0.9606 + 0.9456 + 0.9184) = €274,300

See LOS 57h

59. **A** A synthetic call option is constructed by being long a forward, long the put option, and long or short a zero-coupon bond. Since Anderson proposed a call option where the exercise price was below the forward rate, then this would be a short position in the zero-coupon bond. Put-call-forward parity states that:

$$c_0 + \frac{[X - F(0,T)]}{(1+r)^T} = p_0$$

BPP
LEARNING MEDIA

Rearranging terms a synthetic call option is:

$$c_0 = p_0 - \frac{[X - F(0,T)]}{(1+r)^T}$$

That is you take a long position in the put, a short bond position and a long forward position

See LOS 56i

60. **C** Higher volatility of the underlying will increase the value of call options. Higher strike prices will reduce the value of call options. Higher value of the underlying will increase, not decrease the value of the call option

See LOS 56d